Come Play House

BY EDITH OSSWALD

ILLUSTRATED BY ELOISE WILKIN

SIMON AND SCHUSTER · NEW YORK

THE LITTLE GOLDEN BOOKS ARE PREPARED UNDER THE SUPERVISION OF

MARY REED, PH.D.

FORMERLY OF TEACHERS COLLEGE, COLUMBIA UNIVERSITY

Author and Artist

EDITH OSSWALD, a nursery school specialist, has tested her children's books—among them the Little Golden Book, TOYS—in her work at Teachers College, Purdue, and Yale. ELOISE WILKIN is well known for her illustrations of many juveniles, including THE NEW HOUSE IN THE FOREST, THE NEW BABY, NOISES AND MR. FLIBBERTY-JIB, and FIX IT, PLEASE!

 DESIGNED AND PRODUCED BY THE SANDPIPER PRESS AND ARTISTS AND WRITERS GUILD, INC. PRINTED IN THE U.S.A. BY WESTERN PRINTING AND LITHOGRAPHING COMPANY
PUBLISHED BY SIMON AND SCHUSTER, INC., ROCKEFELLER CENTER, NEW YORK 20, NEW YORK

Visiting

Knock! Knock!
Somebody is at my door.
I wonder who can it be?

Mrs. Smith!
How nice of you!
Come right in and have some tea!

Mail

I am writing a letter.
I will mail it soon.
I want to get an answer
this afternoon.

The Postman

The postman comes.
He rings the bell:
"A letter for you, Mademoiselle!"

The Show

All my dollies sit in a row.
All my dollies
  wait for the show.
The curtain opens.
The show begins.
The monkey bows.

The monkey grins.
He jumps and prances.
He chatters and dances.
He bows very low.
That's the end of the show.

Playing School

I love to play school.
I am the teacher.
My dollie is "Me."
My teddy is the boy next door.
And all my toys are many more
  Children in the class.
Sometimes I stand in front of them
And make them all be good.
Sometimes I work and talk with them
Just as a teacher should.

ABCDEFGH
LMN
OPQRST
YZ
1
2
3
4

The Jungle Gym

The jungle gym is a wonderful place
for doing wonderful things.
It can be a zoo with cages and bars
for monkeys, lions, and tigers.
It can be a house with upstairs and downstairs
for Mummy, Daddy, and Baby.
It can be an airplane, a train or a boat,
a tractor, a digger, a bus.
A jungle gym can be anything.
Now it's a castle and I am king.

Messy Dishes

Messy dishes!
Dirty dishes! Pooh!
In goes the dirty dish.
Out comes the shiny dish.
Clean dishes! Hooh!

Hands in the sudsy water,
Soft and warm.
Messy dishes gone.
All the dishes done.

Baking

Bake a cake.
Bake a cake.
What kind shall it be?
A huge big birthday cake
All for me.

Bake a cake.
Bake a cake.
What icing shall I make?
Sweet pink icing
All over the cake.

Bake a cake.
Bake a cake.
How many candles shall I fix?
One,
Two,
Three,
Four,
Five, or
Six?

Shopping

Icebox empty!
Breadbox empty!
What am I going to eat?
I will have to do some shopping
In the store across the street.

Pocketbook
And shopping bag.
What am I going to buy?
Peanut butter, bread and jelly,
Lollipops and pie.

Dinnertime

Dinner is ready.
Sit down and eat.
We have potatoes
And some meat.

We have carrots and peas —
— Pass me the salt, please.
Thank you, that's nice —
And for dessert, orange ice.

Wedding

Let's play
Wedding today!
I am the bride.
You are the groom.
We dress up
And walk through the room.

First, I must put on a veil.
My dress must be long
And it must trail.
You must wear a flower
In your suit.
Then we walk side by side,
Because you are the groom
And I am the bride.

Mowing the Lawn

The wheels roll smoothly round and round.
The blades whirl with a whizzing sound.
They cut the grass.
It smells so sweet.
It scatters all over
  And tickles my feet.

House Cleaning

Move the chairs
  And move the table.
Move the bed
  And move the crib.
Take the broom
  And sweep the floor.
Swish — swish — swish —

Put back the chairs,
Put back the table,
Put back the bed,
Put back the crib,
Put away the broom.
You cleaned the room.

Valentines

Red paper and doilies,
Scissors and glue.
I am cutting and pasting
A Valentine for you.

The Carpet Sweeper

Dirt and crumbs all over the rug!
I must use the carpet sweeper.
I push it forward.
I pull it back.

The little wheels purr
As they turn around,
But the brush picks up the crumbs
Without a sound.

My Garden

I dig and rake
  And scatter the seeds.
I hoe like Daddy
  To keep out the weeds.
Then popping out here
  And popping out there
  Are onions and lettuce,
  Carrots and peas,
  Beans and potatoes,
  Corn and tomatoes.

Sale

Carrots for sale,
Fresh from my garden!
Ten cents a bunch!
I pulled them this morning.
You can eat them for lunch.
Buy a bunch!
Buy a bunch!

Ironing

What a wrinkled cloth you are!
I know what I must do.
I'll make the iron slip and slide
Right over you!

Pudgy

I fed Pudgy outdoors today.
Jill took his dish and ran away.

The Farmer

My animals make lots of noise.
Listen to them now!
Moo, moo! Baa, baa!
Cluck, cluck! Meow!
Oink, oink! Gobble, gobble!
Quack, quack! Bow, wow!

The Doctor

My dollie fell and hurt her head.
The doctor bandaged it and said:
She must lie very still
Because she's very ill.
Tomorrow night
She will be all right.

Packing

I am going on a trip,
A very long trip,
I am going by train overnight.
I must pack in my suitcase
Whatever I need
To sleep on the train overnight.

Pajamas, washcloth,
Slippers and soap,
Toothbrush, hankies,
Bathrobe and comb.

Moving Out

We are moving!
We are moving!
We are moving today.
All my toys are packed away.

Waiting for the moving men
To put them in the moving van.
They've moved already beds and chairs,
Tables and dressers and lamps downstairs.
The house is so empty!
It's quite a sight.
I wonder where I will sleep tonight.

Moving In

This has been a funny day.
All our furniture moved away.
Out of the old house
Into the new house
Where we will stay.

I didn't know
Where I would sleep tonight.
But when my bed came in,
I was all right!

B